THE ART OF

hand lettering

HOW-TO LESSONS & PRACTICE FOR MODERN CALLIGRAPHY

LILY KATE

Published in 2018 by
Hand Lettering & Calligraphy Books

table of contents

GETTING STARTED

TYPE BASICS

Serif: Serif refers to the feet of a letter. It is the easiest type to read, which is why most books use it for their body type.

Sans Serif: Sans is French for "without." A sans serif font has no feet. It is a great pair for lettering.

Baseline: Refers to the line where your letter sits.

Mean Line: Half the distance between the baseline and your cap height.

Ascender: Extends above the mean line, and can be found in the letters T, H, K, and L.

Descender: Extends below the baseline and can be found in the letters G, Y, P, Q and F.

Downstroke: The downward stroke of your letter that is also the thickest part in calligraphy.

Hairline or Upstroke: Any upstrokes of calligraphy can be referred to as hairline strokes. They are the thinnest part of the letter.

Cross Stroke: The line that crosses through certain letters.

Ascender Line
Mean Line
Base Line
descender
cross stroke
upstroke
downstroke
flourish

Lettering

There are all sorts of lettering styles. These styles tend to differ depending on the type of tools you are using. Traditional calligraphy uses a dip pen and ink, chalk lettering uses chalk, and brush lettering uses brushes or brush pens. Each tool is going to give you a different look and feel to your lettering!

traditional

Tools Used: Pointed pen, Nib, Ink

Different Nibs will produce different looks in traditional calligraphy, depending on the amount of ink it allows to flow. You will notice this mostly in the size of the downstrokes. In traditional calligraphy you apply pressure to your pen with each downstroke of the letter.

Tools Used: Brush and Paint or Brush Pens

Just like traditional calligraphy, each brush will produce different results. Brush calligraphy has a very natural and whimsical look because it has so much texture. It is usually a bit thicker than your traditional calligraphy.

Tools Used: Traditional Chalk

Chalk is a very popular type of lettering. Just like brush lettering, it keeps a lot of it's texture. It can also be manipulated and produce many different types of shades.

free hand lettering

Tools Used: Micron Pen/ Fine tip Pen

This free hand lettering was created with a fine tip pen. It is a monoline script and keeps the same weight throughout the letterforms. This is a popular style because of its versatility.

When it comes to calligraphy styles, it all depends on the pressure applied with your strokes. Traditional and brush calligraphy have the same set of rules. When you are creating your calligraphy letters it is important to remember to apply more pressure on your downstrokes and less pressure on your upstrokes. This is what creates the calligraphy look. This technique is incredibly difficult to master. It is important to remember - practice makes perfect! You'll find plenty of practice later on in the book!

When using chalk as your medium, you will most likely be creating using the faux calligraphy style. You will write your word out first and then go back and create thicker downstrokes, just like I did with the example on the previous page. This mimics the look of traditional calligraphy.

When practicing free hand lettering, the world is your oyster! To recreate the look on the previous page, you will keep the same amount of pressure throughout your letterforms. You can also add in down-strokes after to give it the traditional calligraphy look.

lighter upstroke/
less pressure used

brush

heavy downstroke
more pressure used

mimic calligraphy
downstrokes

faux

draw your word, outline downstrokes, and fill in!

Lettering can be such a great hobby! It can be incredibly soothing and relaxing. Just remember to keep it fun.

Draw slowly + take your time! Really master each letter before trying your hand at any words.

If you find yourself getting frustrated. Take a break and come back to it another time! Remember, this is supposed to be fun!

Everyone eventually develops their own style. Start out by choosing your favorite style and then put your own twist on it! Lettering is all about learning muscle movements and keeping control of your pen. You do not have to have nice handwriting to be a great hand letterer!

Finding your own style will set you apart from anyone else! Once you understand the basic movements and shapes of the letters, it will be easier to manipulate them to create your own different styles.

You will start to notice after running through some of the letter drills that certain letters repeat the same motions. Like the rounded faces of the A,D, G and Q. Once you get a repeating shape down, mastering one letter turns into mastering many!

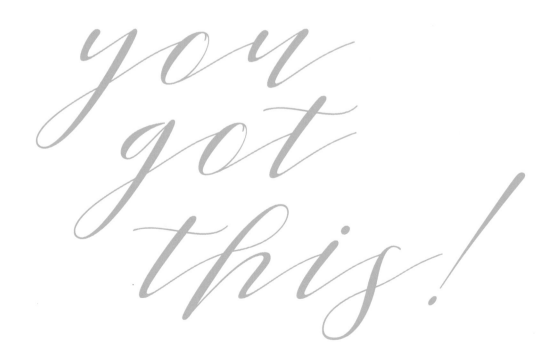

you got this!

LETTER DRILLS

This is a very classic lowercase calligraphy style. Remember to add pressure on your downstrokes!

Start to memorize those muscle movements with each of your letter drills!

a b c d e f g

h i j k l m n

o p q r s t u

v w x y z

a a a

b b b

c c c

d d d

e e e

f f f

g g g

h h h

i i i

j j j

k k k

l l l

u u u

v v v

o o o

p p p

q q q

r r r

s s s

t t t

u u u

v v v

w w w

x x x

y y y

z z z

This is a very modern and loose lowercase calligraphy style. Remember to add pressure on your downstrokes! Start to memorize those muscle movements with each of your letter drills!

a b c d e f

g h i j k l

m n o p q

r s t u v

w x y z

a a a

b b b

c c c

d d d

e e e

f f f

g g g

h h h

i i i

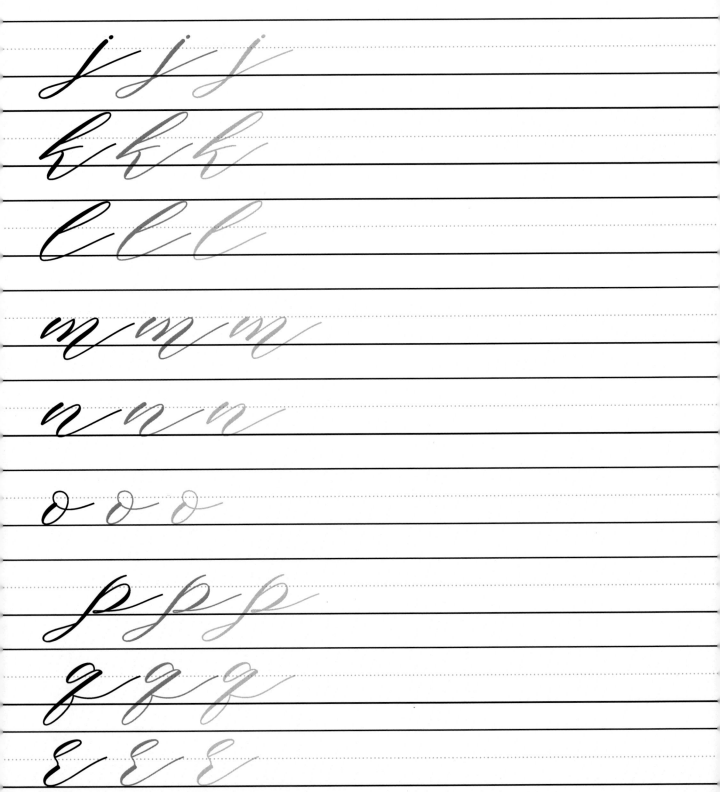

S S S

T T T

u u u

v v v

w w w

x x x

y y y

z z z

This is a very traditional lowercase calligraphy style. Notice the hard angles of each letter.

Remember to add pressure on your downstrokes! Start to memorize those muscle movements with each of your letter drills!

a b c d e f g

h i j k l m

n o p q r s t

u v w x y z

a a a

b b b

c c c

d d d

e e e

f f f

g g g

h h h

i i i

j *j* *j*

k *k* *k*

l *l* *l*

m *m* *m*

n *n* *n*

o *o* *o*

p *p* *p*

q *q* *q*

r *r* *r*

s s s

t t t

u u u

v v v

w w w w

x x x

y y y

z z z

This is a lowercase free letter calligraphy style. Notice the monoline letters—keep the same pressure throughout! Start to memorize those muscle movements with each of your letter drills!

a b c d e f g h

i j k l m n o

p q r s t u v

w x y z

a a a

b b b

c c c

d d d

e e e

f f f

g g g

h h h

i i i

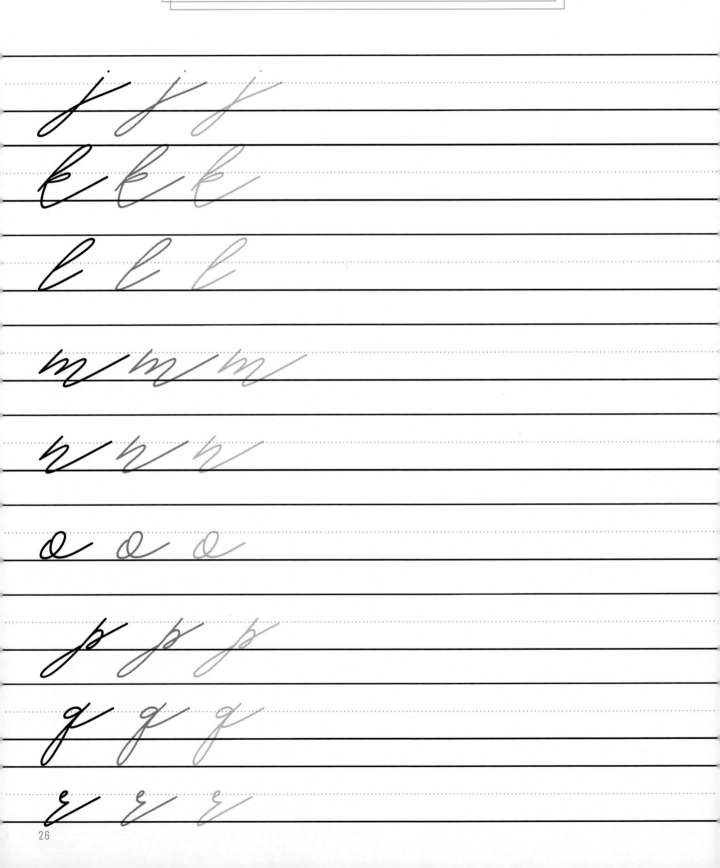

This is a lowercase brush style. Notice the texture in the letters. Remember, keep your hand loose and apply more pressure on the downstrokes!

Start to memorize those muscle movements with each of your letter drills!

a b c d e f g h

i j k l m n o

p q r s t u

v w x y z

a a a

b b b

c c c

d d d

e e e

f f f

g g g

h h h

i i i

j   *j*   *j*

k   *k*   *k*

l   *l*   *l*

m   *m*   *m*

n   *n*   *n*

o   *o*   *o*

p   *p*   *p*

q   *q*   *q*

r   *r*   *r*

s s s

t t t

u u u

v v v

w w w

x x x

y y y

z z z

This is a lowercase faux calligraphy style. Draw the letter, outline your downstroke and fill it in!

Start to memorize those muscle movements with each of your letter drills!

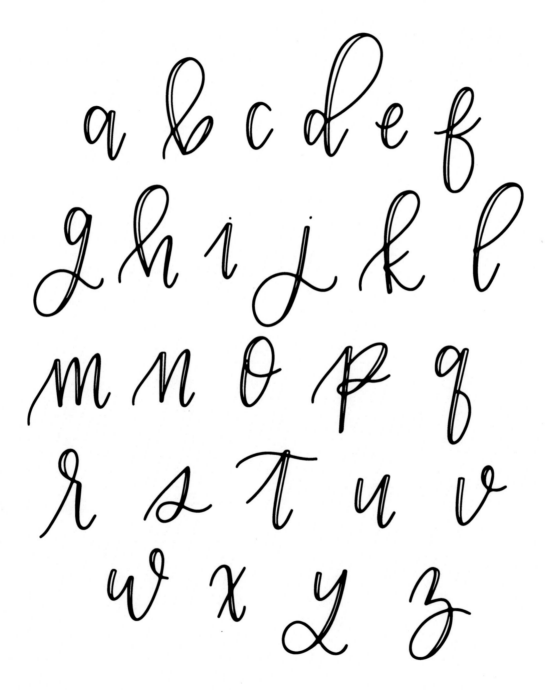

a a a

b b b

c c c

d d d

e e e

f f f

g g g

h h h

i i i

j j j

k k k

l l l

m m m

n n n

o o o

p p p

q q q

r r r

t t t

u u u

v v v

w w w

x x x

y y y

z z z

This is a very traditional uppercase calligraphy style. Notice the hard angles of each letter. Remember to add pressure on your downstrokes!

Start to memorize those muscle movements with each of your letter drills!

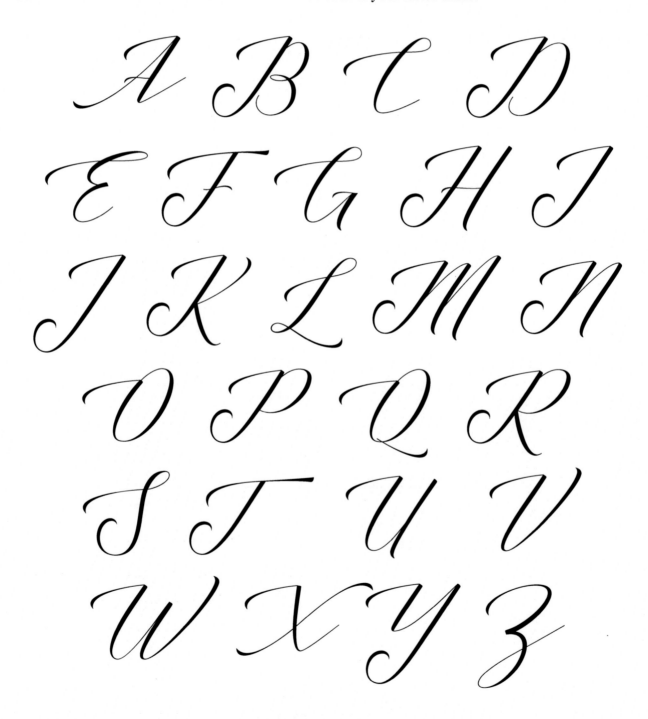

A A A

B B B

C C C

D D D

E E E

F F F

G G G

H H H

J J J

J J J

K K K

L L L

M M M M

N N N

O O O

P P P

Q Q Q

R R R

S S S

T T T

U U U

V V V

W W W

X X X

Y Y Y

Z Z Z

This is a very modern and loose uppercase calligraphy style. Remember to add pressure on your downstrokes!

Start to memorize those muscle movements with each of your letter drills!

CONNECTING THE FORMS

connecting letters

Connecting your letters is the trickiest part of lettering. Unlike when you are writing in cursive, you want to think of each letter as its own shape and form. You will use the tails of your letters to create a bridge between two letters. You can see that above, each letter has the same angled tail that connects it to the next letter. Each letter is drawn separately. You want to make sure you start your next letter close enough to the tail of the letter before it.

note all the connecting tails

hello

hello hello

cheers

note how the E tail turns into the front of the R

cheers cheers

PRACTICE HERE!

lovely

lovely lovely

PRACTICE HERE!

smile

smile   smile

PRACTICE HERE!

happy

happy   happy

PRACTICE HERE!

laugh

laugh   *laugh*

PRACTICE HERE!

WORD DRILLS

WORD DRILLS

winter

spring

summer

fall

autumn

leaves

bloom

WORD DRILLS

beach

shells

ocean

waves

bikini

sand

splash

giraffe

camel

penguin

buffalo

peacock

elephant

gazelle

chocolate

peanut butter

gingerbread

pumpkin

biscotti

macaron

oatmeal

WORD DRILLS

notebook

schedule

weekly

daily

monthly

planner

school

science

math

english

history

gym

art

writing

PROJECTS

WHY

hello there

PRACTICE HERE!

WHY

hello there

PRACTICE HERE!

hello
Darling

PRACTICE HERE!

hello
Darling

PRACTICE HERE!

happy
BIRTHDAY

PRACTICE HERE!

happy
BIRTHDAY

PRACTICE HERE!

PRACTICE HERE!

PRACTICE HERE!

Merry Christmas

PRACTICE HERE!

Merry Christmas

PRACTICE HERE!

Made in the USA
Lexington, KY
18 March 2018